Best Ever
BRAIN
TEASERS

igloobooks

igloobooks

Published in 2016
by Igloo Books Ltd
Cottage Farm
Sywell
NN6 0BJ
www.igloobooks.com

Cover designed by Nicholas Gage
Edited by Caroline Icke

LEO002 0116
2 4 6 8 10 9 7 5 3
ISBN 978-1-78557-004-9

Puzzle compilation, typesetting and design by:
Clarity Media Ltd, http://www.clarity-media.co.uk

Printed and manufactured in China

Contents

A–Z PUZZLE
Each letter of the alphabet from A–Z has been removed from the grid once, to leave 26 empty squares. You must work out which letter from A–Z fits in each of the blank squares and write it in, so as to fill the grid and solve the puzzle.

ARROW WORDS
Answer the clues in the grid in the direction of each arrow to complete the puzzle.

BATTLESHIPS
Locate the position of each of the ships listed in the grid. Numbers around the edge tell you the number of ship segments in each row and column of the puzzle. Ships are surrounded on all sides by water, including diagonally.

BRIDGES
Connect all the circles (which represent islands) into a single interconnected group. The number in a circle represents the number of bridges that connect that island to other islands. Bridges can only be created horizontally or vertically, with no more than two bridges between any pair of islands. Bridges cannot cross any other bridges.

JIGSAW SUDOKU
Place the numbers 1–9 once in each row, column and bold-lined jigsaw region composed of nine cells.

KAKURO
Fill the white squares so that the total in each across or down run of cells matches the total at the start of that run. You must use the numbers from 1–9 only and cannot repeat a number in a run.

KING'S JOURNEY
Deduce the journey of a chess king as it visits each square of the grid exactly once, starting at 1 and ending at 100. The king may move one square in any direction at a time, including diagonally.

KRISS KROSS
Each word must be placed in the grid once to solve the puzzle – you must work out where each word goes in order to complete the grid.

PATHFINDER
Moving from letter to adjacent letter, can you find a path that visits every square and spells out words associated with the given theme? Start on the shaded square.

RECTANGLES
Divide the grid into a series of rectangles or squares, such that every cell is in exactly one region. Numbers indicate the size of each region: for instance a '5' in a cell means that cell is part of a region that contains five cells in total. There is only one number in each region.

No. 1 Kriss Kross

3 letters
Rev
Sap

4 letters
Bean
Flog
Haze
Over
Plot
Step

5 letters
Frets
Globe
Lance
Picks
Quote
Rinse
Tests

7 letters
Alloyed
Impeach
Rounder
Stilton
Sunless

8 letters
Bequests
Birdbath
Endorses
Persists
Roosting
Stylists

10 letters
Allergenic
Atmosphere
Breastbone
Eucalyptus

13 letters
Assertiveness
Professorship

No. 2 Rectangles

										24				2
										7				3
					2	5						3		
					2			3						
					10		3				4		3	3
22						8	2							9
							6		2					
									2					
	30													
				4			2	2						20
2														
			3		5									
4										22				2
2														2

No. 3 A–Z Puzzle

B	U	R	E	A	U		A	B	L	A	Z	E
E			P		B		O					N
M		R	E	P	O	R	T	I	N	G		C
O		E		E		L		E				E
A	D	J	U	N	C	T	S		A	R	T	S
N		O			H		T		M			T
	K	I	C	S		C	Y	N	I	C		
S		N		S	P		P		N			C
E	V	I	L		D	O	V	E	T	A	I	L
P		N	P		S		C		T			A
U		G	R	A	V	I	T	A	T	E		M
R			✓		T		S					P
L	A	N	C	E	T		S	E	A	L	L	S

A B C D E F G H I J K L M N O P Q R S T U V W X Y Z

No. 4 King's Journey

	15		22						38
13					33		42		
	18		25		34		59		
	11			28		62			
	9	2	1	27		66	64		45
					69				46
6		77	76					55	
79	85			91	100	98	72		48
		89	92				96		
		83	88						50

No. 5 Kakuro

No. 6 Pathfinder

T	A	T	S	E	T	N	I	T	R
E	T	B	E	Q	S	T	L	E	E
J	N	N	R	U	E	L	Y	G	V
U	E	M	U	A	G	E	C	A	O
R	Y	J	O	L	I	T	Y	D	C
A	C	D	A	L	Y	R	A	E	S
V	T	I	N	A	T	A	C	C	U
E	A	U	J	I	R	U	D	I	S
T	C	N	U	R	D	I	I	O	E
I	O	N	J	I	S	C	T	N	R

Legal Terms

Accused, Adjournment, Bequest, Caveat, Covert, Injunction, Intestate, Jurisdiction, Jury, Legacy, Legality, Residuary, Trial

No. 7 Jigsaw Sudoku

	3	14 56						
		45 67		1				4
9	4	2	5	3	6	1	8	7
	5	46	7		9		1	
		9	1	4		8		3
		3			5			
		8				9		6
	9	45 6		8		7		
1		45 67						

11

No. 8 Arrow Words

Limb	▼	Bristle	— the line: conformed	▼	Elevated step	▼	Ascot cat (anag)	Instance of buying or selling
Type of resistor	▶		▼		▼		Bart's father in the Simpsons	▼
▶			Seventh Greek letter	▶				
Thurman: Hollywood star	— Ivanovic: tennis star		Russian country house	▶			▼	
▶	▼		Small symbol or graphic	▶				
Engage in spirited fun		Majestic; wonderful	Packs tightly	▶				
▶		▼	Cooked in the oven	Eg English Breakfast	▶			
Final	Health resort		Molten rock	▼	Mythical monster	▶		
Flatten on impact	▼		▼			Unit of current	Mauna — Hawaiian volcano	
Mountain top	▶				— Carter: snooker player	▼	▼	
▶					Sound of a cow	▶		
Cut a joint of meat	Of a low standard	▶			Criticise strongly	▶		

No. 9 Battleships

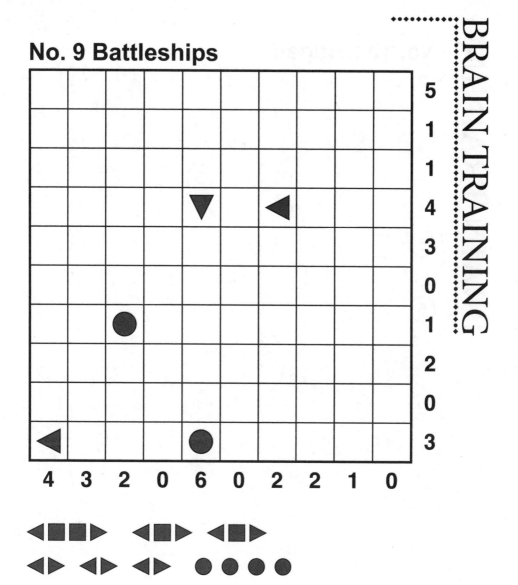

No. 10 Bridges

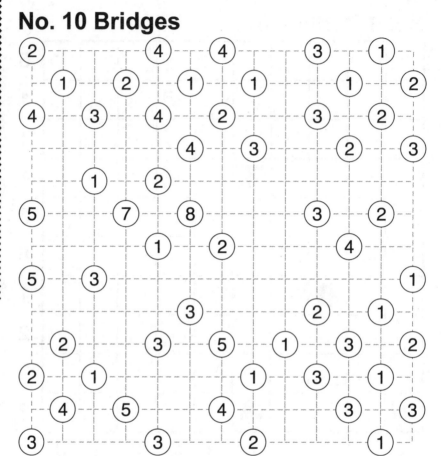

No. 11 Kriss Kross

3 letters
Axe
Gas
Nor
One
Row
Use

4 letters
Asps
Beet
Mono
Nest

5 letters
Ideal
Needs
Ounce
Rearm

6 letters
Bantam
Gospel
Schema
Senses

7 letters
Absolve
Bastion
Cunning
Ejected
Enamels
Kinetic
Octagon
Risotto
Screeds
Smudges
Stomach
Wriggle

9 letters
Arboretum
Pulverise
Reticence
Traveller

No. 12 Rectangles

	3			12									
14						2							
								14					
2	14												
								12					
	2										11	2	
													6
					24								
						2						14	
4			2		4								
2		5				2	3						
								5			10		
	7		6			3				14			
2	3						4						
3					3		7						2

No. 13 A–Z Puzzle

W	E	A	K	E	N	E	D		A	B	A	C
A		F		A		R			A			A
R		F	E	R		O	M	N	I	B	U	S
N		R		T		T			I			E
		A		H		I	N	Q	U	E	S	T
I	D	Y	L	L	I	C		U		S		T
N			L			I						T
V		B		N		E	N	Z	Y	M	E	S
E	N	R	A	G	E	S		Z		I		
R		E			C		I		R			D
S	P	A	T	U	L	A		C	U	R	B	E
E		D			P		A		O			N
S	A	S	H		D	E	C	L	A	R	E	S

A B C D E F G H I J K L M N O P Q R S T U V W X Y Z

No. 14 King's Journey

			1					6	7
45			41	33			13	9	
	68	70							10
48	67		74						
	66	73	76	80			36	29	17
	65			82				28	
				85		98		27	
52	58			96	97	100	89		20
	57				94	93			
				61			24		

No. 15 Kakuro

No. 16 Pathfinder

I	T	A	S	I	T	R	O	M	A
O	K	E	N	I	S	C	V	E	R
N	R	T	R	N	G	U	O	N	R
A	A	E	A	A	E	R	R	T	U
S	M	R	E	L	D	L	E	E	G
S	E	A	R	R	R	A	N	G	A
B	T	E	T	A	E	T	C	T	R
O	T	B	E	S	L	A	Y	M	O
N	S	Y	L	I	L	O	C	Y	T
D	A	N	A	N	D	E	M	N	I

Financial Terms

Amortisation, ~~Analyst~~, ~~Asset~~, ~~Bear~~ Market, ~~Bond~~, ~~Collateral~~, ~~Currency~~, ~~Dealer~~, Earnings, Indemnity, Mortgage, Rates, Turnover

No. 17 Jigsaw Sudoku

		7	6			2	3	
					7	4	1	
8					3		2	
	1	4				8	5	7
				2	1	6		
3							8	
			3					
		2					4	

21

BRAIN TRAINING

No. 18 Arrow Words

Venomous snakes	▼	Sheets of floating ice	▼	Snip		▼	Metric unit of capacity		▼		Free from doubt
Musical instrument with wire strings ▶				▼							
Pierce		Away from home					Benefit				Prestigious TV award
▶								▼			
Exploit unfairly		Happening		Dutch cheese ▶							
▶		▼	Stick to a surface	▼		Vitality ▶					
Muscular tissue	Intense light beam		Impress a pattern on			Nay (anag) ▶					
▶	▼			▼		Gelatinous substance		Pound: US poet	Long grass		
Mammal with a sticky tongue ▶						▼		▼			
Study the night sky ▶											
Hold tightly		Scanty ▶									
▶				Peruse ▶							

22

No. 19 Battleships

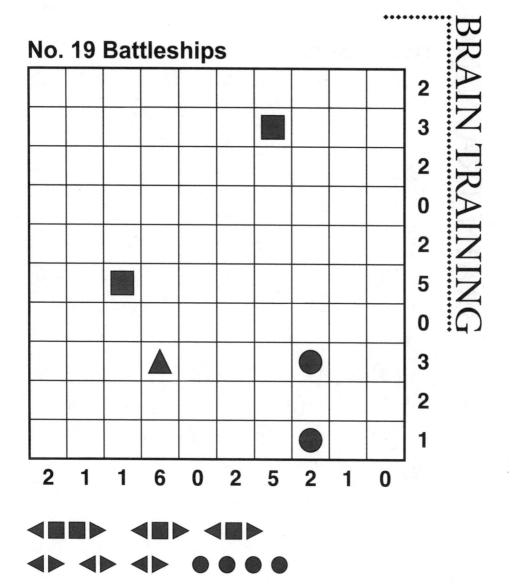

No. 20 Bridges

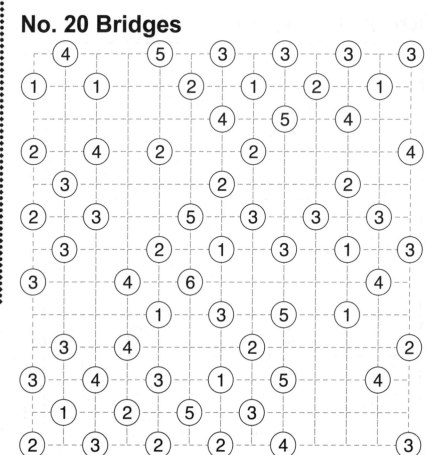

No. 21 Kriss Kross

3 letters
Asp
Ego
Rue
Tor
Was
Woo

4 letters
Achy
Dhow
Door
Nuts
Puma
Stir

5 letters
Askew
Delay
Limes
Other
Remit
Rooms

6 letters
Asleep
Critic
Deemed
Nymphs
Poncho
Rashly
Tartan
Uncork

7 letters
Artwork
Bouncer
Offices
Parasol
Synonym
Tussock

9 letters
Empirical
Mechanics
Microwave
Petroleum

25

No. 22 Rectangles

1	2	3	4	5	6	7	8	9	10	11	12	13
	2		5									
			4							12		
5						2	6					
						24						
	3											5
	2						8					
	4		26									
		7										3
	2	9										
	10	3				2		8				
								2			27	3
		6									6	
											12	
		2					4					
		4					7					

No. 23 A–Z Puzzle

A	L	G	A			B	E	A	U	T	A		H
L		E		R		N		N		V			E
L	Y	C	H	E	E	S		O	Z	O	N	E	
S		K		M		E		B		C			L
P	R	O	V	I	D	E	N	T	I	A	L		
I				N		N		A		D		D	
C	U	S	P	I	D			I		O	N	O	
E		I		S		C		N				W	
	E	X	A	C	E	R	B	A	T	I	O	N	
T		T		E		E		B		M		T	
O	C	E	A	N		C	A	L	Y	P	S	O	
W		E		C		H		E		E		W	
S	I	N		E	R	E	D		C	L	A	N	

A B C D E F G H I J K L M N O P Q R S T U V W X Y Z

No. 24 King's Journey

29			26						19
		33		35	36	37		21	
			52			48	40		
55				76	74				16
	79		93					42	
58		100	98	94			45		14
	82	99	97						
				89		70	12		8
61		84	86			1		7	
	63	65							5

No. 25 Kakuro

No. 26 Pathfinder

O	E	O	F	O	T	E	R	C	E
A	C	R	K	W	R	M	O	I	S
T	H	S	R	O	U	N	E	G	R
K	T	H	R	P	O	E	R	H	O
A	H	E	A	T	M	M	O	C	N
H	G	R	G	A	L	A	U	P	A
Y	I	L	R	R	E	S	S	I	L
A	T	H	A	E	O	I	H	I	S
S	R	O	N	L	K	R	H	G	N
I	G	A	L	I	R	I	S	K	I

Epsom Derby Winners

Galileo, Generous, High-Rise, Kahyasi, Kris Kin, Lammtarra, North Light, Oath, Pour Moi, Secreto, Shergar, Slip Anchor, Workforce

No. 27 Jigsaw Sudoku

2			3		1	6		
					8	4	7	
		1				3	8	
	4			6				
			4	7	2			
			2				1	
	7							5
8						2		

No. 28 Arrow Words

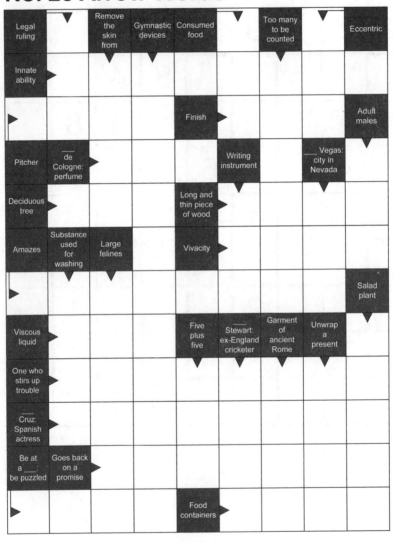

Legal ruling	▼	Remove the skin from	Gymnastic devices	Consumed food	▼	Too many to be counted	▼	Eccentric
Innate ability ▶		▼	▼			▼		
▶				Finish ▶				Adult males
Pitcher	___ de Cologne: perfume	▶			Writing instrument		___ Vegas: city in Nevada	▼
Deciduous tree ▶				Long and thin piece of wood ▼			▼	
Amazes	Substance used for washing	Large felines		Vivacity ▶				
▶	▼	▼						Salad plant
Viscous liquid ▶				Five plus five	___ Stewart: ex-England cricketer	Garment of ancient Rome	Unwrap a present	▼
One who stirs up trouble ▶				▼	▼	▼	▼	
___ Cruz: Spanish actress ▶								
Be at a ___: be puzzled	Goes back on a promise ▶							
▶				Food containers ▶				

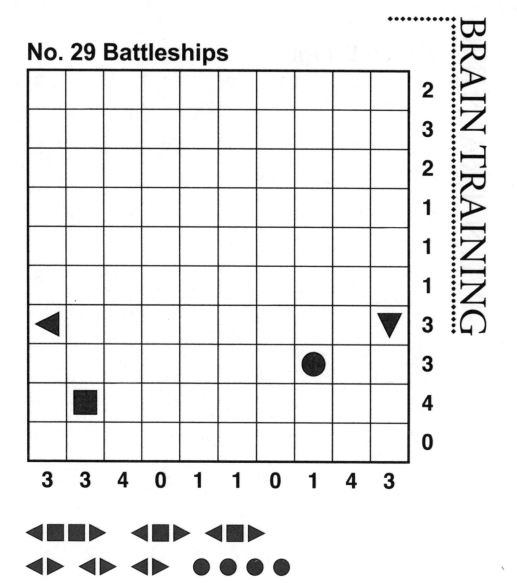

No. 29 Battleships

Row clues (top to bottom): 2, 3, 2, 1, 1, 1, 3, 3, 4, 0

Column clues (left to right): 3, 3, 4, 0, 1, 1, 0, 1, 4, 3

No. 30 Bridges

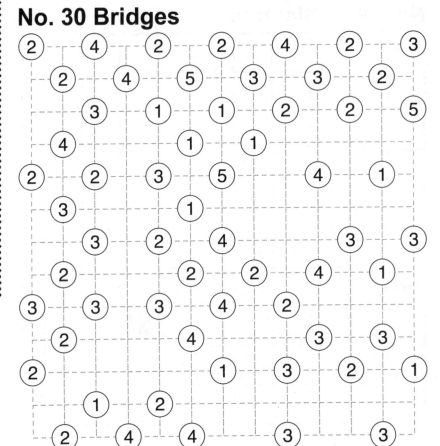

No. 31 Kriss Kross

3 letters
Arc
Pet

4 letters
Moor
Need

5 letters
Chock
Thump
Trend
Usury

6 letters
Acacia
Anorak
Cloves
Invest
Skimpy
Stoker

7 letters
Accrued
Cassock
Erosion
Frontal
Hairnet
Issuing
Leading
Scorned

8 letters
American
Aromatic
Emperors
Hollowed
Solecism
Uncovers

9 letters
Recovered
Sunbather

35

No. 32 Rectangles

14						5							
		6		24		2			8				9
						9					15		
			3										3
2	8								21			3	
				14			2		4			5	
									3				2
	2		5				6						5
	2		4										
	2					8							
	2		6									21	

No. 33 A–Z Puzzle

S	C	R	I	B	E	■	B	R	E	E	Z	Y
■	O	N	■	R	■	I	■	Q	■	E	■	■
E	N	D	S	■	R	E	S	C	U	I	N	G
■	T	■	P	■	S	■	C	■	A	■	■	■
P	I	Q	U	E	■	S	U	B	L	I	S	T
■	N	■	T	■	F	■	I	■	■	A	■	■
S	Y	P	E	R	L	A	T	I	V	E	L	S
■	E	■	■	A	■	S	■	E	■	V	■	■
E	S	C	H	E	W	S	■	S	T	R	A	Y
■	■	E	■	L	■	A	■	E	■	T	■	■
J	O	L	L	I	E	S	T	■	R	A	I	D
■	I	■	I	■	S	■	O	■	A	■	N	■
A	L	E	■	E	S	■	M	A	N	A	G	E

A B C D E F G H I J K L M N O P Q R S T U V W X Y Z

No. 34 King's Journey

	28				24	12		9	
30									7
	100	99		90		83	22		
		97	94		87			15	
34		96		88	81	76		16	
						75		17	
	46	53	57			73			
		47	52			71	69	66	1
	41				59		67		64
39			43						

No. 35 Kakuro

No. 36 Pathfinder

R	T	E	P	Y	H	E	F	S	A
E	S	A	L	O	S	E	B	S	U
A	C	S	C	T	U	M	T	A	G
E	L	L	A	T	E	D	S	A	E
T	E	R	I	D	R	C	R	O	R
A	D	C	O	R	E	A	M	L	O
R	I	A	M	H	G	L	P	L	E
T	C	N	O	A	U	O	E	P	I
C	S	S	R	S	A	M	G	A	T
O	N	E	S	T	L	B	C	O	T

English Cuisine

Cider, Clotted Cream, Cordials, Cottage Pie, Mushy Peas, Ploughman's, Roast Beef, Roast Lamb, Sausage Roll, Scones, Treacle Tart

No. 37 Jigsaw Sudoku

					9			
4				3				7
			2					
						2		
	6							1
		3	4			5	1	
	2			7		3	5	
	5	4			2	7		

No. 38 Arrow Words

23rd Greek letter	Secret agent	▼	Blazes	Thin piece of wood	Opera texts	Drink	Cowboy films	▼
►			Piece of bread ►		▼	▼		
Event which precedes another ►							Woodwind instrument	
►			Head monk ►				▼	
Cereal grass	Agree or correspond		Social division in some societies ►					
Greenish blue colour	▼	Type of deer	▼	Seal of the Archbishop of York ►				
►				Adolescent ►				
Swiftness		Large US feline		Office table		Melt	— Berra: baseball player	
►		▼		▼		▼		Implore
Hollow conduit ►				Cooking appliance ►				▼
►				Mature ►				
Small notes	Diving bird ►			Hairpiece ►				

No. 39 Battleships

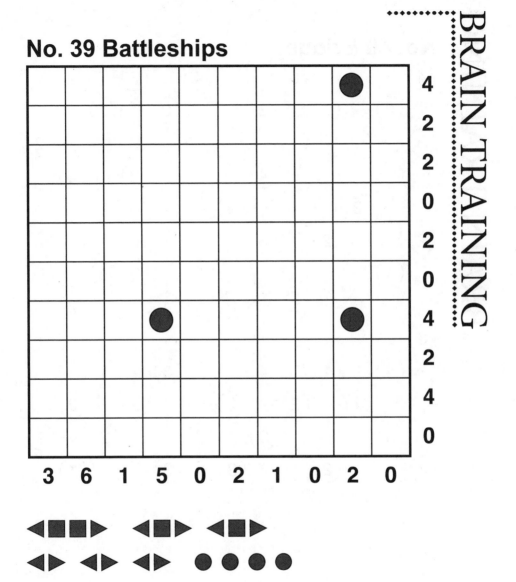

43

No. 40 Bridges

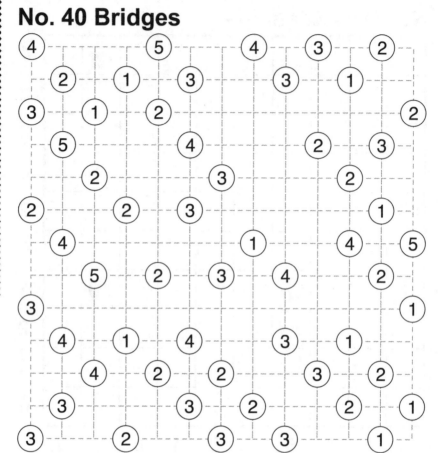

No. 41 Kriss Kross

3 letters
Emu
Pat

4 letters
Barb
Dolt
Dour
Edgy
Lido
Tend

5 letters
After
Stuck
Sweep
Urban

6 letters
Dipole
Leaned
Lulled
Rookie
Sleeve
Sticks
Trolls
Weeded

7 letters
Edifice
Realise

8 letters
Accorded
Attacked
Befuddle
Borrowed
Doubtful
Enrolled
Idealist
Yearbook

10 letters
Retirement
Structured

45

No. 42 Rectangles

1	2	3	4	5	6	7	8	9	10	11	12	13
3									5	3	5	
								8				
				30								8
7												
								2				
	2	4					27				10	
			2	2				3				
	2	2	7							15		4
				4								
					3							
									7	11		
	9				4				2			
	4	2										
			8				15		2			3

46

No. 43 A–Z Puzzle

■	S	P	R	E	A	D	S	H	E	E	T	■
	I	■	X	■	E	■	A	■	A	■		C
	T	■	A	M	B	E	R	■	S	I	R	
G	L	E	A	M	■	A	■	M	■	E		
	O	■	P	■	R	■	S	I	L	K		S
E	Q	U	A	L	I	S	E	■	■	■		T
R	■	S	■	E	■	■	■		U			F
N	■	■	■	I	N	S	I	G	N	I		A
A	B	U	Z	Z	■	A	■	A	■	R	■	L
U	■	N	■	A	■	V	■	T	R	A	I	L
B	I	C	■	I	R	I	S	H	■	W	■	E
S	■	L	■	R	■	E	■	E	■	E	■	N
■	N	E	C	E	S	S	A	R	I	L	Y	

A B C D E F G H I J K L M N O P Q R S T U V W X Y Z

47

No. 44 King's Journey

			69		83		91		
62								87	89
	67								10
	73		95		3	4	6	11	
59	74			100		1		13	12
	75	78	99	98	50	21		15	
56				51		47		19	
40						46			
		42	43			32		27	
				34			28		25

No. 45 Kakuro

No. 46 Pathfinder

B	R	E	A	G	U	O	L	R	I
H	E	L	U	L	E	S	D	F	E
C	A	L	B	C	P	P	U	S	N
U	K	O	C	R	E	L	L	Y	D
O	F	T	C	E	J	O	O	C	S
T	A	S	L	C	N	A	N	T	A
N	T	N	U	B	N	T	S	T	C
I	S	E	C	A	I	U	R	B	O
P	K	V	Q	U	A	B	E	L	W
E	E	E	L	A	I	C	O	S	S

Networking

Acquaintance, Breakfast Club, Colleagues, Contacts, Jolly, Keep In Touch, Old Friends, Rub Elbows, Social Events, Supper Club

No. 47 Jigsaw Sudoku

							8	
1								
9			3					
	6	4						1
		2						
7					4			
8		5			9			7
5		6					2	
4			7				1	

51

No. 48 Arrow Words

Excellent serve	▼	Assumed proposition	▼	Everett: English actor	Piece of jewellery	▼	Military blockade	Walked quickly
Totally uninformed	▶		▼				▼	▼
▶				Sagacious	Louse egg	▶		
Profound	Follow a winding course (of a river)		▼					
Squashed	Title of a married woman	▶			Before the present	▶		
▶								
Not real or genuine	Deceptive manoeuvre	Breathe heavily at night	Attach to		Striped animal		Chunk	
▶		▼		▼		▼	Distribute playing cards	▼	Document of ownership
Not necessary	▶						▼	▼
Male offspring	▶			Venerable ___: English monk	▶			
▶				Road ___: anger when driving				
Ewer (anag)	Breathed out	▶						

No. 49 Battleships

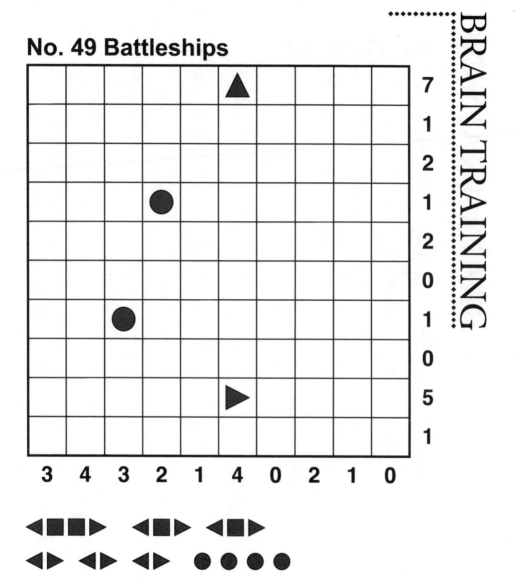

53

No. 50 Bridges

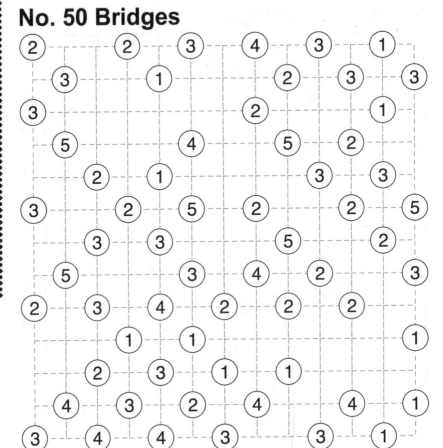

No. 51 Kriss Kross

3 letters
Awl
Elf
Lea
Lee
Lye
Phi
See

4 letters
Bank
Colt
Date
Eddy
Espy
Foes
Lurk
Onto
Wits
Yelp

5 letters
Doyen
Poser

6 letters
Expand
Retina

7 letters
Adamant
Auditor
Curlews
Locusts
Offbeat
Outwork
Scrappy
Tremolo

8 letters
Heighten
Placable
Scenario
Sleepily

9 letters
Reliquary
Sidetrack

No. 52 Rectangles

	4									4		
		2		10	2							
									2			4
4					3							
									4			
								24			10	
			26									
				9								
	14			3				6		14		2
				3		4						
	5					2			4		6	
				7								
				6		3	4					
10	5											3
			5				4		4		3	

No. 53 A–Z Puzzle

S	H	R	E	W	D	L	Y		A	Q	U	A
I		A		A		I				U		S
D	O	Z	E	S		V	E	S	B	E	L	S
E		O		H		E			L			I
		R		C		R	E	J	E	C	T	S
D	I	S	P	L	A	Y			H			T
I				O			K					E
S		B		T		E	M	E	R	A	L	D
F	L	I	G	H	S	S				G		
U		N			T				G			E
S	H	A	C	R	L	E			E	N	O	N
E		R			E			E		D		V
S	O	Y	A		E	M	I	S	S	A	R	Y

A B C D E F G H I J K L M N O P Q R S T U V W X Y Z

57

No. 54 King's Journey

14			32	34			37		
				62					
	18	30	64	87					41
	19			91				59	
	20		67		93		84		46
9	21		68	100	98		83		47
	22	26			99			56	
		25		75	96		80	55	
	6						78		50
4			1	72					

No. 55 Kakuro

No. 56 Pathfinder

B	M	E	L	T	S	O	M	M	E
A	Y	C	R	A	I	T	M	A	T
L	S	I	B	P	H	W	O	L	L
I	L	V	I	H	O	N	T	S	O
T	E	T	N	A	M	E	C	A	P
H	N	I	M	P	A	R	A	O	H
O	O	E	N	A	T	C	E	N	E
P	H	T	S	N	S	A	H	O	N
A	M	S	A	A	D	R	P	O	L
R	I	M	B	R	E	U	M	X	Y

Percussion Instruments

Castanets, Cymbals, Lithophone, Maracas, Marimba, Metallophone, Snare Drum, Timpani, Tom-tom, Vibraphone, Whistle, Xylophone

No. 57 Jigsaw Sudoku

	1				3			
							5	
6	4							2
		3			9			
				4		6		
		2	5	1				
	8			9	4		1	
							4	
			6		8			

61

No. 58 Arrow Words

Country one lives in	Supervise	Confusion (3-2)	——— Duncan Smith: politician	Involuntary spasm	▼	Looks slyly	▼	Varied mixture of things
►	▼	▼	▼					Creature with pointed ears
By way of	►			Give up one's rights	►			▼
Depart	►			Former measure of length	►			
Flee	►			Prying	Sporting official (abbrev)	►		
►			Lacking warmth; bleak	►				Hot spring
Small viper		Yearned for	▼	Tibetan Buddhist monk	Single in number	Spirit in a bottle	Favouring extreme views	▼
Concluding section	►	▼		▼			▼	
Medicinal creams	Fatuously	►						
►								
Wife of a knight	Large period of time	►			Anger	►		
►				Scorch	►			

No. 59 Battleships

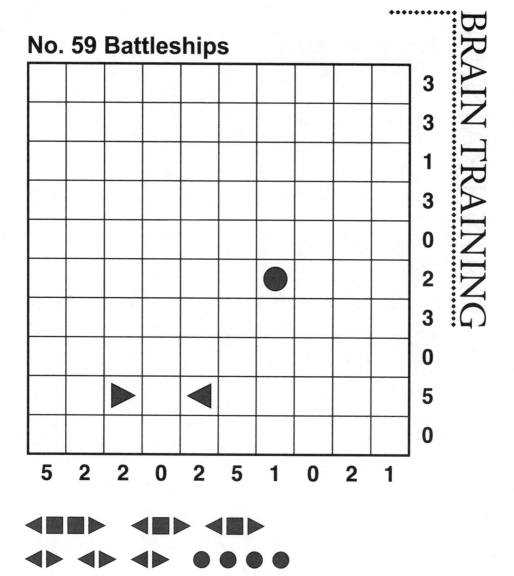

No. 60 Bridges

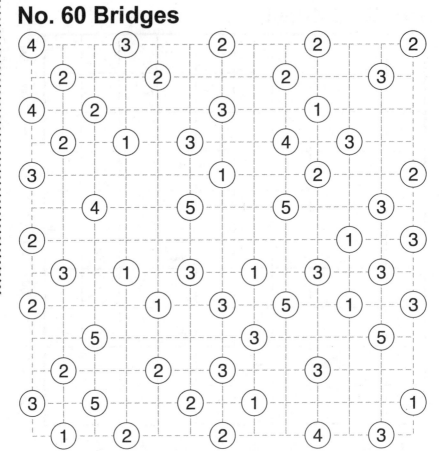

No. 61 Kriss Kross

3 letters
Ago
Ail
Cue
Emu
Erg
Gas
Ion
New
Oaf
Rue

5 letters
Debar
Decry
Rates
Terse

6 letters
Caviar
Demean
Opines
Outlet
Racing
Rapier

7 letters
Baggage
Precise

8 letters
Backstop
Royalist

9 letters
Checklist
Hardliner
Involving
Ointments

10 letters
Bewildered
Cooperator
Digression
Grapefruit

No. 62 Rectangles

2	2		2							18		
	2											
			4	5		2				6		9
										4		
		8										
								24		2		
			2			8					3	
					4		8			2		
	21				4							
						2				3		
				2		2						4
												2
30									24			
						8					6	

No. 63 A–Z Puzzle

	O		S		I		S		T		M	
A	R	C	H	I	T	E	C	T	U	R	A	L
	A		A		C		A				J	
F	L	A	G	S	H	I	P				E	S
			G		I		E		D		S	
B	A	S	I	N	G		G	O	A	T	S	
	E			G		Q				I		
A	A	E			S	Y	B	J	E	C	T	
A		E				A		O				
S	I	G	N			N	E	Y	D	E		
		I		A		G		F		A		
V	E	N	T	R	I	L	O	Q	U	I	S	T
		H		R		S		L		Y		

A B C D E F G H I J K L M N O P Q R S T U V W X Y Z

No. 64 King's Journey

	71		74	81	95	94		91	
				82					
50	68			83	85	99	100	88	
			77					61	
					64				
44	46			54	55	56	57		
16			41				37	33	
		20		22	23		1	31	
13			19				25	28	29
		10		6	5				

No. 65 Kakuro

No. 66 Pathfinder

W	M	R	E	O	S	I	S	E	T
E	R	V	H	T	G	Y	S	A	I
A	E	A	N	L	O	E	T	T	L
T	H	C	E	O	R	O	E	E	L
D	N	O	O	N	P	R	M	I	T
E	N	S	I	D	E	E	N	O	C
T	R	A	T	R	E	S	S	I	I
E	E	T	E	M	H	T	N	O	D
M	R	A	M	O	I	S	A	R	E
P	E	T	U	R	E	O	B	P	R

Weather Words

Condensation, Depression, Isobar, Isotherm, Meteorology,
Prediction, Satellites, Temperature, Thermometer, Weather Vane

70

No. 67 Jigsaw Sudoku

	7	8					3	4
5		4	8					
			9	1				
	6			7			9	
				3				5
3								
	1	6						
4	3	7						

No. 68 Arrow Words

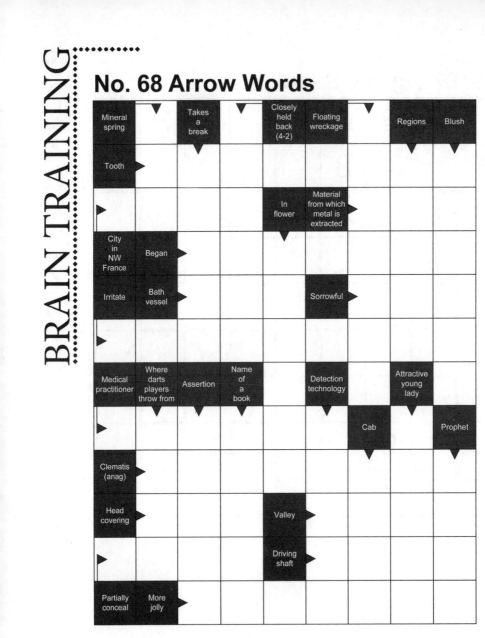

No. 69 Battleships

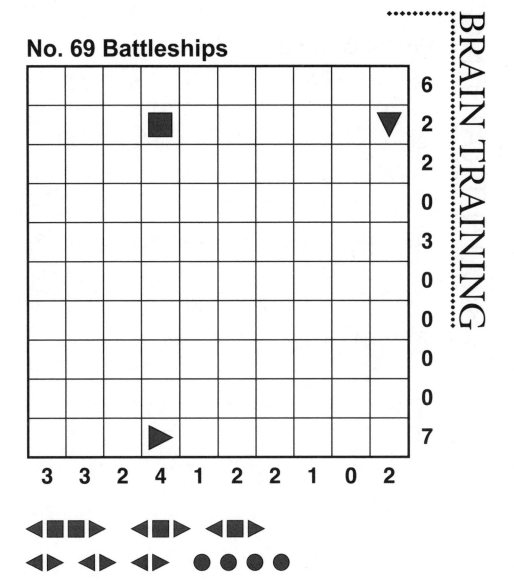

No. 70 Bridges

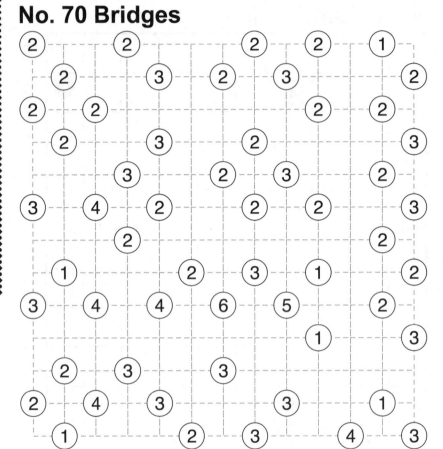

No. 71 Kriss Kross

3 letters
Chi
Ire
Let
Spa
Van
Via
Yak

4 letters
Apse
Bloc
Idea
Kite
Neat
Pity
Puce
Roll
Swab
Vase

5 letters
Empty
Ports

6 letters
Squads
Tirade

7 letters
Accrues
Aerobic
Bejewel
Caldera
Emulate
Parvenu
Prairie
Vibrant

8 letters
Levitate
Plastics
Tartness
Untimely

9 letters
Eavesdrop
Reckoning

75

No. 72 Rectangles

			5		2		2			3			
	2		3					3					2
3									6	6		7	2
			12		4	11		2	3				
									10				3
			12	6									
											2		12
20													
							4	3		12	6		
5	2							3					
		4				4							
	3				4		4						
			9	2				2					
		5	2					2		2			4

No. 73 A–Z Puzzle

A B C D E F G H I J K L M N O P Q R S T U V W X Y Z

No. 74 King's Journey

	47		50	83	82			66	
			86				70		
			88				73		
43				98	94	79		72	
	54		99	100	93			61	
					77			1	3
37		40	56					6	
			34	33	32				5
21	23	24				28	13	11	
			17	16	15			10	

No. 75 Kakuro

BRAIN TRAINING

No. 76 Pathfinder

A	C	A	E	L	T	I	J	U	A
I	L	N	R	I	A	A	N	A	N
C	U	M	O	A	C	U	A	R	A
O	C	A	P	L	D	A	J	A	S
U	L	N	L	I	A	L	A	L	T
P	U	P	A	G	U	U	H	L	I
A	E	B	C	I	X	A	A	L	O
C	A	L	P	U	E	M	U	E	L
A	I	R	A	A	T	O	H	O	N
O	G	N	A	R	U	D	I	H	C

Mexican Cities

Acapulco, Chihuahua, Culiacan, Durango, Guadalajara, Irapuato, Leon, Mexicali, Morelia, Naucalpan, Puebla, Saltillo, Tijuana

No. 77 Jigsaw Sudoku

			7				5	
	5							
3	9	6				8		
2	6							
4	3				1		2	
			1		4			
	4							
		8						5
		3						

No. 78 Arrow Words

Expel; drive out	▼	Heavenly body	▼	Distant	▼	Type of tree	Table support	▼
North American nation (abbrev)		▼		Famous English racetrack		Not wet	Cheek (slang)	
Sit with legs wide apart				▼		▼	▼	
▶			Indian garments	▶				
Ate (anag)	Cyclone		Vault under a church	▶				
Card game for one	▼	Shrub with glossy leaves	Have as a purpose		Andre ___; tennis player	Blocks of metal	Expressing regret	
▶		▼				▼	▼	
Hurried	▶			Antelope	▶			Great ___; breed of dog
Eg almond or pecan				Matured	▶			▼
Metric unit equal to 100 square metres				Settee	▶			
Secret retreat	▶			Amaze	▶			
Ancient	▶			___ of Wight; English island	▶			

No. 79 Battleships

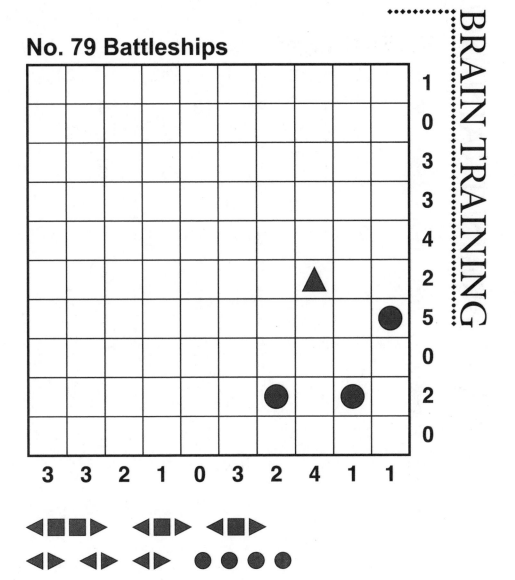

No. 80 Bridges

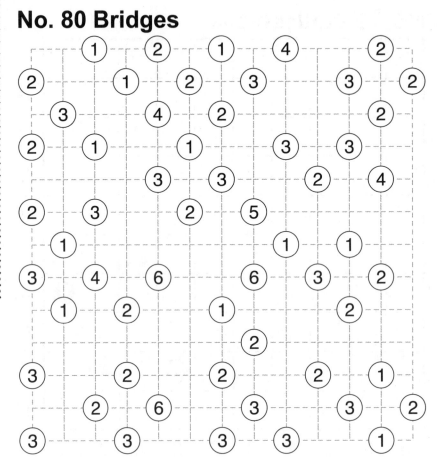

No. 81 Kriss Kross

3 letters
Eel
His
Old
Tow

4 letters
Coax
Copy
Levy
Plod

5 letters
Anger
Ketch
Music
Swirl

6 letters
Jetsam
Parent
Sawyer
Sodium

7 letters
Brushed
Cuirass
Elicits
Rampage
Regroup
Unaided
Yielded

8 letters
Academic
Carapace
Forsaken
Nowadays
Promised
Scorches
Securely
Township

9 letters
Ampersand
Bystander
Clubhouse

No. 82 Rectangles

			20											
2											8			
						3							2	
		8												
		2				2			18					4
		2												
10			18											
	10			20						27				
						2			7					
														9
						3						9		
							15							
					6									4
	2						2				10			

No. 83 A–Z Puzzle

C	O	D	E	S				F		T	A	P
	D		E		S	P	I	E	R			I
A	D	U	L	A	T	E		Z		A		L
	B		S		W			Z	O	N	A	L
S	A	W	B	O	N	E	S					A
	L		N		R		P					R
G	L	O	B	A	L		Q	U	E	E	N	S
L		V		L		A		R			A	
O		E		I	N	F	I	N	I	T	Y	
W	O	R	T	H		N		F			T	
I		L		U		E	X	I	S	T	E	D
N		A	F	F	I	X		E			R	
G	U	N		F		A	S	S	I	S	T	

A B C D E F G H I J K L M N O P Q R S T U V W X Y Z

No. 84 King's Journey

	76		79						
	77			83			43	41	37
73	86	88				49	47		
		90	95		100	50			
68					98		34		31
				93			26		29
		64		53	24		1		
	61	62			18	2			6
	59							9	
57			20		15	13	12	10	

No. 85 Kakuro

No. 86 Pathfinder

E	V	E	G	A	G	N	E	E	N
R	N	D	D	E	I	O	R	H	O
S	O	A	I	C	V	C	D	P	S
A	C	L	R	E	E	R	L	E	S
T	E	T	P	U	G	N	A	H	F
I	N	O	N	E	N	O	H	P	F
O	E	R	U	O	R	C	A	L	I
N	K	B	M	T	A	P	O	L	R
S	A	E	A	Y	R	E	O	E	A
P	E	R	S	H	E	L	L	R	T

Telephone Words

Caller, Conversation, Cordless Phone, Dial Tone, Engaged, Hang Up, Operator, Phone Number, Receiver, Say Hello, Speaker, Tariff

No. 87 Jigsaw Sudoku

				8				
7								3
				4			6	
9								7
				5				
	1	2				4	3	
							2	6
	2						8	
	4			7	5			

No. 88 Arrow Words

Caress and kiss	Pamper	Be in debt	▼	Birds of prey (6,6)	▼	Hits hard	Spiny egg-laying mammal	▼
▶	▼	▼				Story	___ vera: used in cosmetics	
Nocturnal bird of prey ▶				US state ▶		▼	▼	
Was in first place ▶				African country ▶				
Church song		Mother		Trudge				
▶		▼		Observed ▶				
Signal for action ▶				Follows closely	At some point in the past	Make law	Fight (3-2)	
▶				▼	▼	▼	▼	Check; exam
Red fruits eaten as vegetables		Large seabird ▶						▼
Fragile ▶								
Dr ___: US writer		Votes into office ▶						
▶					Very small child			

No. 89 Battleships

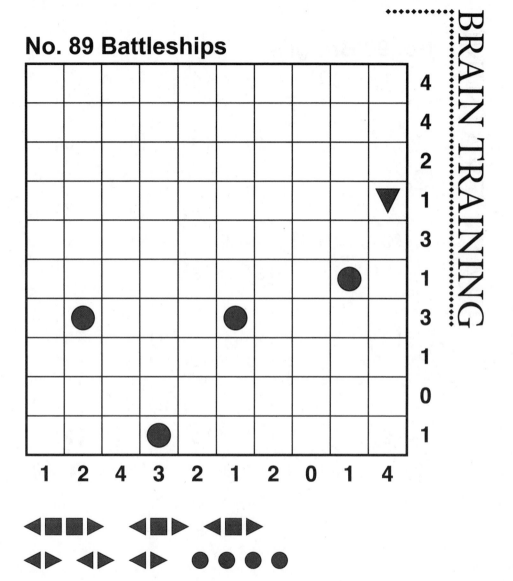

No. 90 Bridges

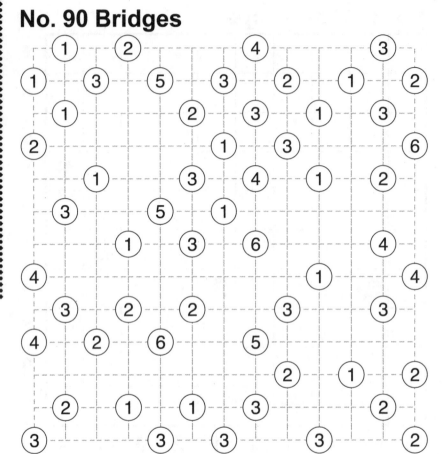

No. 91 Kriss Kross

3 letters
Ace
Arc
Ill
Nor
Oar
Owl
Pea
Phi
Ria
Tor

5 letters
Eagle
Isles
Lasts
Mamba

6 letters
Atonal
Biceps
Cravat
Gravel
Lollop
Marmot

7 letters
Archery
Cordial

8 letters
Greatens
Motorist

9 letters
Homeowner
Interpret
Practiced
Repressed

10 letters
Containers
Convergent
Factitious
Princesses

No. 92 Rectangles

		4	2									3	
					15						3		
3		3		3								12	
					10								
						2					3		
	16					2							
	2	3		2		6							
								24		10			
3	24												5
4					9								
			15				3						
				2									
				2									
				6			24						

No. 93 A–Z Puzzle

A	P	P	A	L	█	S	N	O	O	K	E	R
S	█	O	U	█	A	█	█	B	█	E	█	█
P	█	S	N	█	F	█	B	E	A	R	D	█
A	U	T	O	C	R	A	T	█	E	█	I	█
R	█	B	H	█	R	█	A	S	H	E	D	█
A	C	A	D	E	M	I	C	█	T	█	█	A
G	█	G	█	D	█	█	L	█	M	█	█	R
U	█	█	█	S	E	R	E	N	A	D	E	█
S	H	O	W	Y	█	█	G	█	T	█	█	D
█	A	E	█	A	T	T	U	T	U	D	E	█
L	I	T	R	E	█	I	█	Q	█	R	█	V
█	█	█	█	█	█	C	█	█	E	█	█	I
Q	U	E	E	N	L	Y	█	Y	O	D	E	L

A B C D E F G H I J K L M N O P Q R S T U V W X Y Z

97

No. 94 King's Journey

					55	70		91		
	39			69					100	95
34		52		68			98			
33	41		58					88	97	
	42		59			75	86	85		
	43		60			65				81
		47		61		3	1			
26		45		20	18	4			79	
		28			14	12			9	
										7

No. 95 Kakuro

No. 96 Pathfinder

A	P	K	E	C	A	O	T	C	A
E	P	A	C	E	R	R	L	E	K
I	L	E	C	T	O	C	C	D	E
N	W	U	R	A	L	O	H	U	D
R	O	M	A	S	K	P	P	R	O
B	S	B	L	A	A	A	L	T	U
E	S	L	E	D	B	L	E	S	G
M	N	E	K	I	A	E	M	N	H
T	O	B	A	C	E	C	H	U	T
E	M	A	E	R	C	A	E	P	S

Desserts

Apple Crumble, Apple Strudel, Baked Alaska, Brownie,
Carrot Cake, Chocolate Cake, Doughnuts, Eton Mess, Ice Cream,
Peach Melba

100

			3		6			
					9	4	7	
						2		
	1					3		
			4	6			1	
	5	9			2			3
	2		8					
		1	7					

No. 98 Arrow Words

Sport in which Beth Tweddle excelled	▼	Lower in rank	▼	Highly excited	▼	What one hears with	Dual audio	Your (poetic)
Least old ▶						▼	▼	▼
Tina (anag)		Popular beverage		Curse; solemn promise ▶				
▶		▼		Dull colour				
Very long period of time ▶					Eg Andrew Motion	Eight-sided shape		Computer keyboard users
▶				Kind of beet ▶		▼		▼
Russian sovereign		Come to a point	Loud resonant noise	▼	Bashful; reluctant to give details ▶			
Skin irritation ▶		▼	▼		Mother		Corrode	
Squid ▶					▼		▼	
▶								
Green vegetable	Last in a series ▶							
Unit of energy ▶			Tiny social insects ▶					

No. 99 Battleships

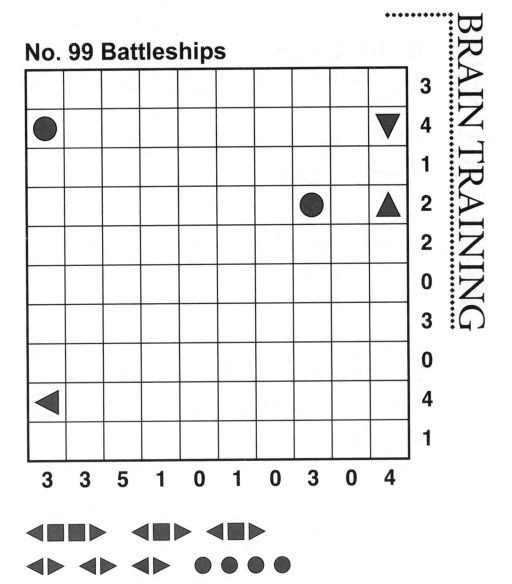

No. 100 Bridges

No. 101 Kriss Kross

3 letters
Aid
Tea

4 letters
Afar
Drum
Gags
Once

5 letters
Corgi
Smack

6 letters
Advice
Asides
Chirps
Curdle
Gateau
Lodges
Nodded
Quaver
Stymie
Tenant

7 letters
Ageless
Laconic
Reminds
Sloshed

8 letters
Curative
Unloaded

9 letters
Ingenuous
Liquidate
Lowercase
Quickness

10 letters
Cantilever
Didgeridoo

105

No. 102 Rectangles

3		12											
							24					10	
										2		3	2
											3		
2									13				3
				6			2						
	6		4				2	2	2				
				8									2
				4		3			2				
		6	2				2		2	24			3
	6												
			4					15		4			
						2							
3					12	2							
	3										15		

No. 103 A–Z Puzzle

C	H	I	L	L	I		F		V		B	
R		D		N	A	U	T	I	C	A	L	
A	L	L		D	R		R	S				
T		I	N	S	E	C	T		T	E	A	R
E		N		X		H		U		L		
R	O	G	U	E		R	E	S	O	R	T	S
		N		I		R		S				
S	U	G	G	E	S	T		L	I	E	G	E
	T		R	O		Q			R			V
Y	O	G	A	S	O	U	N	D	S			O
	P	T	E	A				A	S	R		
I	Y	E	A	R	L	D		T		E		
A		D	S	S	E	I	Z	E	S			

A B C D E F G H I J K L M N O P Q R S T U V W X Y Z

107

No. 104 King's Journey

		63				58			
		72	74	75		59		42	
	70			80	79		56		37
68		5	82				55		36
			2	87	86	85		45	
7			1				96	53	46
	11					100		47	
	20				98			48	
		23	91					31	
	15	17					27		29

No. 105 Kakuro

BRAIN TRAINING

No. 106 Pathfinder

P	M	R	A	W	S	S	E	E	B
O	A	T	I	M	B	B	E	E	D
L	N	N	O	O	N	O	R	S	L
L	I	S	Y	C	E	P	D	W	I
I	C	O	E	N	E	H	X	A	W
A	D	B	H	O	R	O	N	E	S
L	O	O	X	L	U	M	O	H	O
B	O	S	E	C	S	T	E	R	N
E	R	B	I	N	O	L	E	E	E
E	B	R	U	S	H	O	C	B	Y

Beekeeping

Bee Brush, Beeswax, Brood Box, Cluster, Colonies, Drone, Honeybee, Honeycomb, Pheromones, Pollination, Social, Swarm, Wild Bees

No. 107 Jigsaw Sudoku

		8					1	
	4	2				8		
	5							
	9					6		
			2				4	
			7					
7			6				8	
			9		5			
	8	4						2

No. 108 Arrow Words

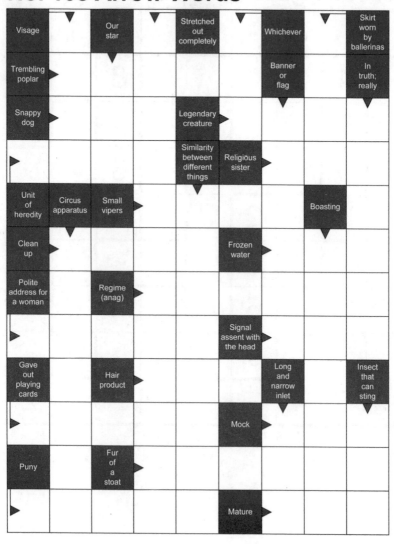

No. 109 Battleships

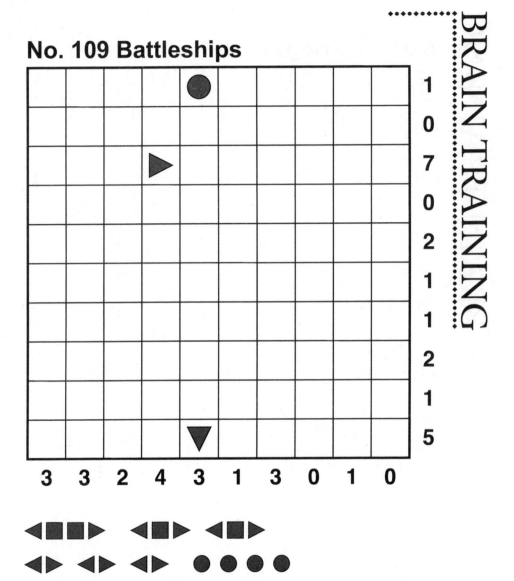

No. 110 Bridges

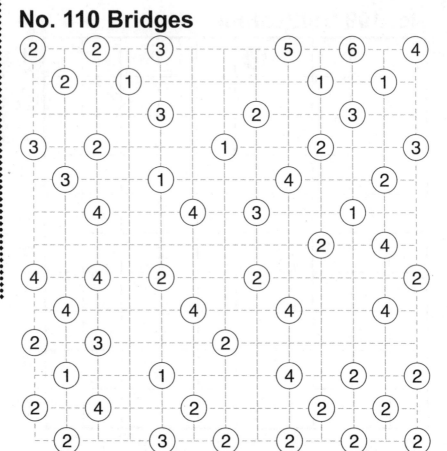

No. 111 Kriss Kross

3 letters
Cot
Lop

5 letters
Anger
Climb
Fauna
Giddy
Learn
Maids
Raids
Rhyme

6 letters
Accrue
Gothic
Intake
Scoops
Stasis
Unsure

7 letters
Aseptic
Earmark
Oddball
Parsecs
Riposte
Shutter
Spotted
Unhitch

9 letters
Accretion
Aggressor
Obscurity
Reclining

11 letters
Stimulation

No. 112 Rectangles

C1	C2	C3	C4	C5	C6	C7	C8	C9	C10	C11	C12	C13	C14	C15	C16
						15									
										25				3	
6			2												
2			2									3			
2	2	2	2		10							2	8		5
							9				5				
	4													28	
		2	2												
			2												
				16											
	9			2	4										
						27									
3				3											
		9								5			2	2	

No. 113 A–Z Puzzle

G	R	E	E	T	I	N	G	■	D	E	B	T
■	O	■	■	M	■	H	■	■	E	■	A	■
L	O	G	J	A	M	■	O	C	T	E	T	S
■	S	■	O	■	E	A	R	■	R	■	H	■
S	T	A	G	■	N	■	L	O	A	V	E	S
■	E	■	■	■	S	■	■	C	■	■	■	■
U	R	T	A	K	E	■	B	O	T	T	O	M
■	■	R	■	■	■	A	■	■	R	■	■	■
S	Q	U	A	R	E	U	■	P	A	I	N	■
■	U	■	M	■	N	A	T	■	H	■	M	■
L	O	B	U	S	T	■	I	S	O	B	A	R
■	T	■	T	■	E	■	T	■	T	■	M	■
C	A	S	H	■	R	H	E	T	O	R	I	C

A B C D E F G H I J K L M N O P Q R S T U V W X Y Z

No. 114 King's Journey

	72	80		85	87				
	73		82	84		89		100	93
69		77					99		
				8		5		96	
64	66	67			1		12	17	
		35				3			
	60			36			15	21	
58	57		47			31			22
53		50	48					27	
			43		40	39		26	

No. 115 Kakuro

No. 116 Pathfinder

C	A	I	C	R	O	V	E	E	N
R	L	M	H	C	W	A	O	V	W
E	C	E	E	L	B	Y	R	E	A
L	U	U	Q	L	A	O	T	T	T
U	L	O	R	R	Y	L	T	H	C
R	A	T	S	A	I	D	H	E	R
P	A	T	P	E	E	R	M	O	M
M	G	S	D	E	T	T	E	A	P
A	E	O	O	M	E	E	R	T	E
T	S	P	E	R	U	S	A	E	M

Numbered Objects

Calculator, Cheque, Diary, Lottery Ball, Microwave, Oven, Postage Stamp, Ruler, Speedometer, Tape Measure, Thermometer, Watch

No. 117 Jigsaw Sudoku

No. 118 Arrow Words

Carlisle: US singer	▼	Type of diving (4-3)	▼	Deviate from the subject at hand	Stage of twilight	The military (5,6)	Inhabited by ghosts	▼
►					▼	▼	Decline in value	
Male athletes		Belonging to us		Official language of Pakistan ►			▼	
►		▼						
Barker: former tennis star ►				Retained ►				
►					Dr ___: US record producer ►			
Stanza of a poem		Terminate		Uncovered	Gave a meal to ►			
One more than five	Suggestion	▼	Coalition of countries	▼				Small insect
►	▼		Mock		Fix the result in advance ►			▼
Beloved ►			▼		Metal container ►			
Disliked intensely		Unit of money ►						
►					Become firm ►			

No. 119 Battleships

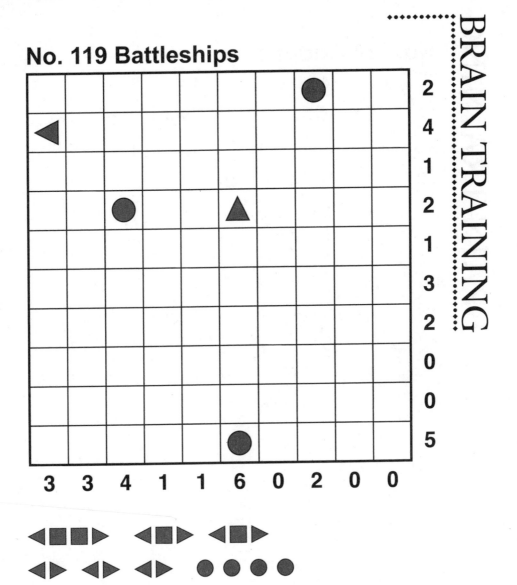

No. 120 Bridges

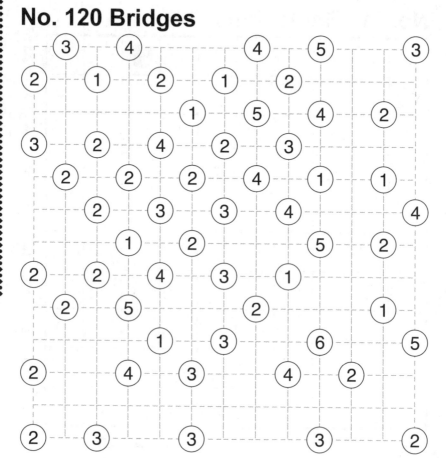

No. 121 Kriss Kross

3 letters
Ant
Ion

4 letters
Came
Coop
Hint
Item
Lets
Raft

5 letters
Abyss
Balsa
Norms
Owner

6 letters
Escudo
Fusion
Kisses
Ordain
Robust
Shears
Snares
Worthy

7 letters
Issuing
Locales

8 letters
Adorable
Armchair
Canteens
Clueless
Memorise
Overcoat
Recorder
Supplant

10 letters
Locomotive
Nomination

No. 122 Rectangles

										6		
			12					16			2	2
			4							2		
			3		4					2		
2								10		7		
	2	3					3					
	4				4				4			
			12									24
									3			
4												
	18							4				
												5
5		3	2	2	4	9	8			4	5	5
									2	2		5
	3				3		3	3				

No. 123 A–Z Puzzle

A		P			S		P		K		
X	Y	L	O	P	H	O	N	E		U	S	E
L		A			R		E		D		N
E	X	T	R	A		R	A	V	I	O	L	A
S		F		S		O		E			T
	O	S	H	A	W				Y	T	H	S
H		R				D		O			S
A	L	M	S		A	Q	U	E	O	U	S
L			B		U		V		N		S
C	L	I	M	E	R	A		A	U	G	U	T
Y		C		E		R		G		K		A
O	N	E		F	U	R	I	O	U	S	L	Y
N		S		Y		Y		N			T	S

A B C D E F G H I J K L M N O P Q R S T U V W X Y Z

No. 124 King's Journey

		10			88	90			98
14			7			91	95	100	
	16	2	4						82
18			1			85	84		
20				57		77	79		
		27	56		73			70	68
23		53	55						66
	51				61				43
			49	48		46	45		
31	32				37		39		

No. 125 Kakuro

No. 126 Pathfinder

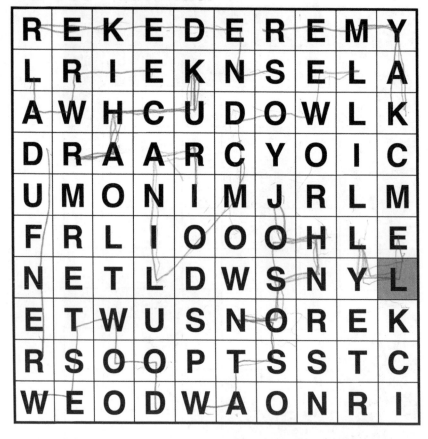

R	E	K	E	D	E	R	E	M	Y
L	R	I	E	K	N	S	E	L	A
A	W	H	C	U	D	O	W	L	K
D	R	A	A	R	C	Y	O	I	C
U	M	O	N	I	M	J	R	L	M
F	R	L	I	O	O	O	H	L	E
N	E	T	L	D	W	S	N	Y	L
E	T	W	U	S	N	O	R	E	K
R	S	O	O	P	T	S	S	T	C
W	E	O	D	W	A	O	N	R	I

Ryder Cup Golfers

Dufner, Johnson, Kaymer, Kuchar, Lawrie, Lyle, McDowell, McIlroy, Molinari, Poulter, Snedeker, Stricker, Watson, Westwood, Woods

No. 127 Jigsaw Sudoku

								4
	6	5						
2								
8	1							6
5			8		9	2	1	
	4							
6						7		1
	3				4			
		2						

No. 128 Arrow Words

	Back of the neck	Alert and thinking cogently (5-6)	▼	Without affection	Breathe hard	Amazing	Gives off light	Dry (of wine)
Surround ▶	▼	▼			▼	▼	▼	▼
Every ▶				Arthur ___: former US tennis player ▶				
Overly concerned with detail ▶								
▶				Not (anag)				Expressed gratitude
Repast	Cereal grass ▶			Item for catching fish ▶				▼
Large waterbirds	Avoid	▼	Express one's opinion	Shallow food container ▶				
▶	▼		▼		Jackie ___: famous actor		Extent of a surface	
Vessel ▶				Male person ▶			▼	
___ Sandler: comedian ▶				▼	Annoy ▶			
Someone in custody ▶								
Biblical garden ▶					Wander aimlessly ▶			

No. 129 Battleships

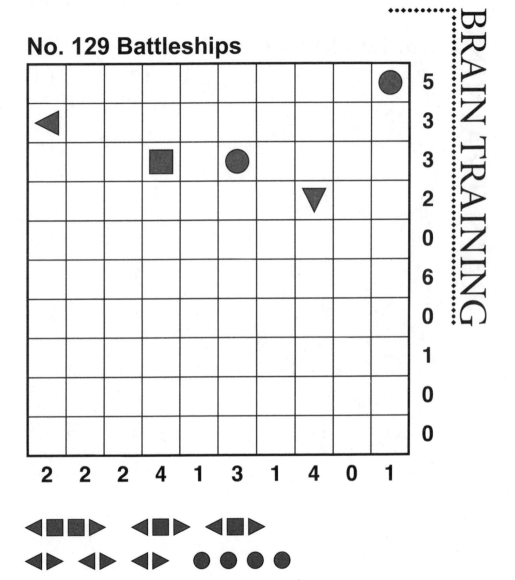

No. 130 Bridges

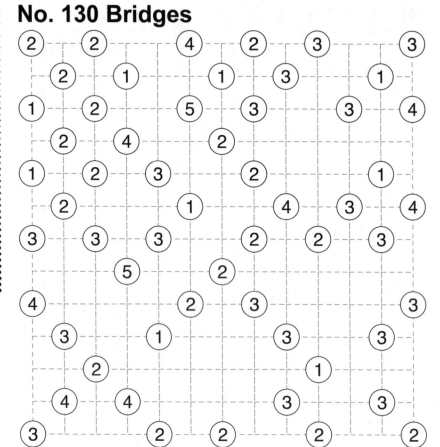

134

No. 131 Kriss Kross

3 letters
Ego
Lie
Odd
Shy
Tar
Tea

4 letters
Aide
Herb
Lyre
Saga

5 letters
Aspic
Eaten
Heron
Viola

6 letters
Adsorb
Animal
Bottle
Sedate

7 letters
Closest
Drawers
Illicit
Initial
Linings
Markers
Ominous
Rectify
Rentals
Rituals
Tallies
Wrapped

9 letters
Beginning
Bimonthly
Decathlon
Oblivious

No. 132 Rectangles

									12			3	
			15										
2							2				3		2
			6	2								14	
			3		3								
	10										6		
				16		12		8		2		7	
						2	2				7		
18									4				
													8
						2			20				
			5		2					7			
					7								
			4	3							2	2	2

No. 133 A–Z Puzzle

C		Z	C			B		J		S
H	E	I	G	H	T		F	O	R	E	S	T
O		P		A		R		Y		R		A
C	A	P	S	I	L	E		H	I	R	E	R
K		E		N		C		O		Y		T
E	A	R	S		S	T	O	O	L		
R		S		C		A		D				T
			G	O	O	N	S		E	U	R	Y
A		A		E		G		S				P
R	E	M	I	T			L	E	C	T	U	R	E
O		O		I		E		O		N		S
S	L	U	I	C	E		O	F	F	I	C	E
E		R		T				F				T

A B C D E F G H I J K L M N O P Q R S T U V W X Y Z

SOLUTIONS

Solution 1

Solution 2

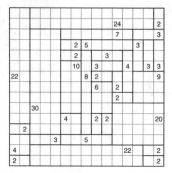

Solution 3

Solution 4

14	15	16	22	23	31	32	36	37	38
13	17	21	24	30	33	35	42	41	39
12	18	20	25	29	34	60	59	43	40
10	11	19	26	28	61	62	63	58	44
8	9	2	1	27	67	66	64	57	45
7	5	4	3	68	69	70	65	56	46
6	78	77	76	75	74	73	71	55	47
79	85	86	90	91	100	98	72	54	48
80	84	87	89	92	99	97	96	53	49
81	82	83	88	93	94	95	52	51	50

Solution 5

Solution 6

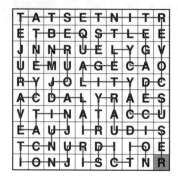

SOLUTIONS

Solution 7

6	3	1	4	9	8	2	7	5
5	8	7	3	1	2	6	9	4
9	4	2	5	3	6	1	8	7
8	5	4	7	6	9	3	1	2
2	6	9	1	4	7	8	5	3
7	1	3	8	2	5	4	6	9
3	7	8	2	5	1	9	4	6
4	9	5	6	8	3	7	2	1
1	2	6	9	7	4	5	3	8

Solution 8

Solution 9

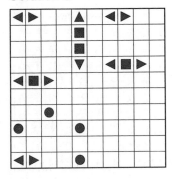

Solution 10

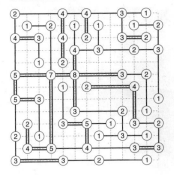

Solution 11

Solution 12

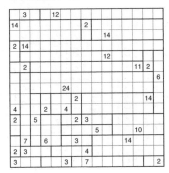

139

SOLUTIONS

Solution 13

Solution 14

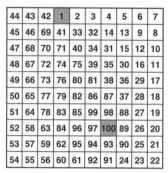

44	43	42	1	2	3	4	5	6	7
45	46	69	41	33	32	14	13	9	8
47	68	70	71	40	34	31	15	12	10
48	67	72	74	75	39	35	30	16	11
49	66	73	76	80	81	38	36	29	17
50	65	77	79	82	86	87	37	28	18
51	64	78	83	85	99	98	88	27	19
52	58	63	84	96	97	100	89	26	20
53	57	59	62	95	94	93	90	25	21
54	55	56	60	61	92	91	24	23	22

Solution 15

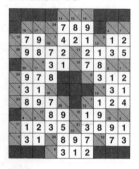

Solution 16

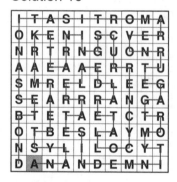

Solution 17

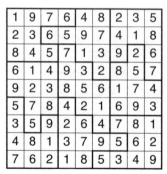

1	9	7	6	4	8	2	3	5
2	3	6	5	9	7	4	1	8
8	4	5	7	1	3	9	2	6
6	1	4	9	3	2	8	5	7
9	2	3	8	5	6	1	7	4
5	7	8	4	2	1	6	9	3
3	5	9	2	6	4	7	8	1
4	8	1	3	7	9	5	6	2
7	6	2	1	8	5	3	4	9

Solution 18

SOLUTIONS

Solution 19

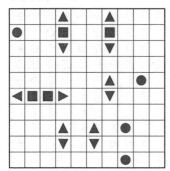

Solution 20

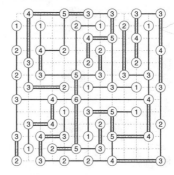

Solution 21

Solution 22

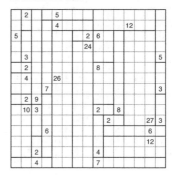

Solution 23

Solution 24

29	28	27	26	25	24	23	22	20	19
30	32	33	34	35	36	37	38	21	18
31	54	53	52	51	50	48	40	39	17
55	56	78	77	76	74	49	47	41	16
57	79	80	93	92	75	73	46	42	15
58	81	100	98	94	91	72	45	43	14
59	82	99	97	95	90	71	44	13	9
60	83	85	96	89	88	70	12	10	8
61	64	84	86	87	69	1	11	7	6
62	63	65	66	67	68	2	3	4	5

SOLUTIONS

Solution 25

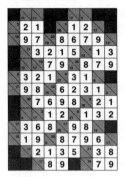

Solution 26

Solution 27

2	8	7	3	4	1	6	5	9
3	5	9	6	2	8	4	7	1
4	6	1	7	9	5	3	8	2
7	4	3	5	6	9	1	2	8
5	1	8	4	7	2	9	6	3
9	2	6	8	1	4	5	3	7
6	9	5	2	8	3	7	1	4
1	7	2	9	3	6	8	4	5
8	3	4	1	5	7	2	9	6

Solution 28

Solution 29

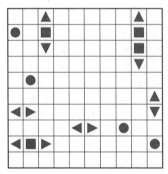

Solution 30

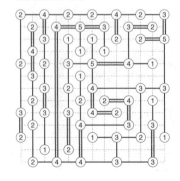

SOLUTIONS

Solution 31

Solution 32

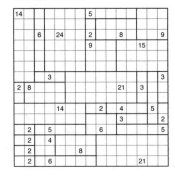

Solution 33

Solution 34

29	28	27	26	25	24	12	11	9	8
30	31	92	91	85	84	23	13	10	7
32	100	99	93	90	86	83	22	14	6
33	98	97	94	89	87	82	21	15	5
34	55	96	95	88	81	76	20	16	4
35	54	56	79	80	77	75	19	17	3
36	46	53	57	78	74	73	70	18	2
37	45	47	52	58	72	71	69	66	1
38	41	44	48	51	59	68	67	65	64
39	40	42	43	49	50	60	61	62	63

Solution 35

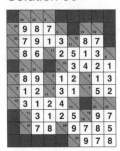

Solution 36

SOLUTIONS

Solution 37

5	1	7	8	6	9	4	3	2
4	9	2	5	3	8	1	6	7
6	3	1	9	4	7	8	2	5
3	7	5	2	1	4	6	9	8
9	4	6	1	8	5	2	7	3
2	6	8	7	5	3	9	4	1
7	8	3	4	2	6	5	1	9
8	2	9	6	7	1	3	5	4
1	5	4	3	9	2	7	8	6

Solution 38

Solution 39

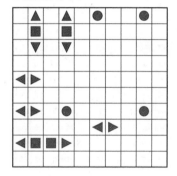

Solution 40

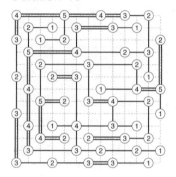

Solution 41

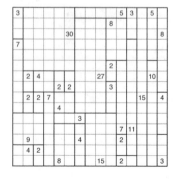

Solution 42

(grid puzzle)

144

Solution 43

Solution 44

Solution 45

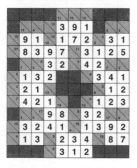

Solution 46

Solution 47

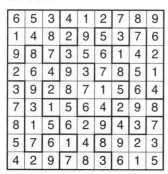

Solution 48

SOLUTIONS

Solution 49

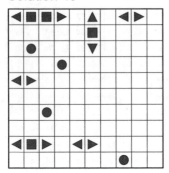

Solution 50

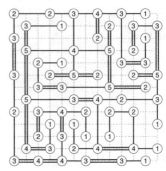

Solution 51

Solution 52

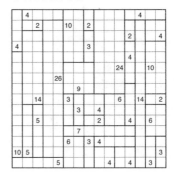

Solution 53

Solution 54

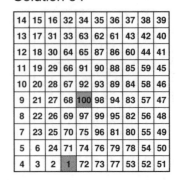

146

SOLUTIONS

Solution 55

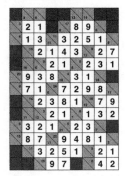

Solution 56

B	M	E	L	T	S	O	M	M	E
A	Y	C	R	A	I	T	M	A	T
L	S	I	B	P	H	W	O	L	L
I	L	V	I	H	O	N	T	S	O
T	E	T	N	A	M	E	C	A	P
H	N	I	M	P	A	R	A	C	H
O	O	E	N	A	T	C	E	N	E
P	H	T	S	N	S	A	H	O	N
A	M	S	A	A	D	R	P	O	L
R	I	M	B	R	E	U	M	X	Y

Solution 57

2	1	5	8	7	3	4	6	9
3	9	7	4	6	2	1	5	8
6	4	1	9	8	5	3	7	2
4	6	3	1	2	9	7	8	5
9	5	8	3	4	7	6	2	1
8	7	2	5	1	6	9	3	4
7	8	6	2	9	4	5	1	3
5	2	9	7	3	1	8	4	6
1	3	4	6	5	8	2	9	7

Solution 58

Solution 59

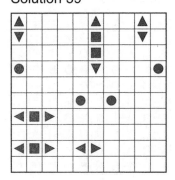

Solution 60

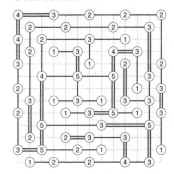

SOLUTIONS

Solution 61

Solution 62

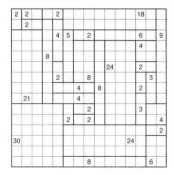

Solution 63

Solution 64

70	71	73	74	81	95	94	93	91	90
69	72	75	80	82	96	97	98	92	89
50	68	76	79	83	85	99	100	88	60
49	51	67	77	78	84	86	87	61	59
45	48	52	66	65	64	63	62	58	35
44	46	47	53	54	55	56	57	36	34
16	43	42	41	40	39	38	37	33	32
15	17	20	21	22	23	24	1	31	30
13	14	18	19	8	7	2	25	28	29
12	11	10	9	6	5	4	3	26	27

Solution 65

Solution 66

148

SOLUTIONS

BRAIN TRAINING

Solution 67

1	7	8	6	2	5	9	3	4
5	2	4	8	9	3	7	1	6
6	4	3	9	1	7	2	5	8
2	6	5	1	7	4	8	9	3
7	9	1	4	3	2	6	8	5
9	8	2	3	5	6	1	4	7
3	5	9	7	6	8	4	2	1
8	1	6	5	4	9	3	7	2
4	3	7	2	8	1	5	6	9

Solution 68

Solution 69

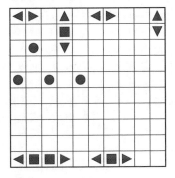

Solution 70

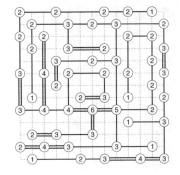

Solution 71

Solution 72

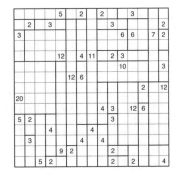

149

SOLUTIONS

Solution 73

Solution 74

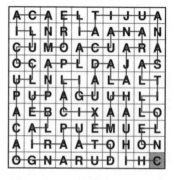

46	47	49	50	83	82	69	68	66	65
45	48	51	86	85	84	81	70	67	64
44	52	87	88	96	95	80	73	71	63
43	53	89	97	98	94	79	74	72	62
42	54	90	99	100	93	78	75	61	2
38	41	55	91	92	77	76	60	1	3
37	39	40	56	57	58	59	30	6	4
22	36	35	34	33	32	31	29	7	5
21	23	24	25	26	27	28	13	11	8
20	19	18	17	16	15	14	12	10	9

Solution 75

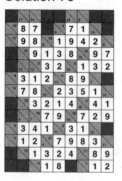

Solution 76

Solution 77

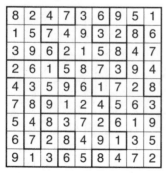

8	2	4	7	3	6	9	5	1
1	5	7	4	9	3	2	8	6
3	9	6	2	1	5	8	4	7
2	6	1	5	8	7	3	9	4
4	3	5	9	6	1	7	2	8
7	8	9	1	2	4	5	6	3
5	4	8	3	7	2	6	1	9
6	7	2	8	4	9	1	3	5
9	1	3	6	5	8	4	7	2

Solution 78

SOLUTIONS

Solution 79

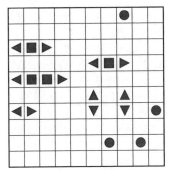

Solution 80

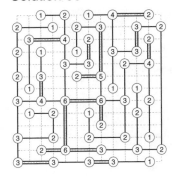

Solution 81

C	O	A	X		S	C	O	R	C	H	E	S
A		N		T	O		A		I		E
R	E	G	R	O	U	P		M	U	S	I	C
A		E		W		Y		P			U
P	A	R	E	N	T		S	A	W	Y	E	R
A			S		C		G		I		E
C	L	U	B	H	O	U	S	E		E	E	L
E		N		I		I		L		L		Y
	A	M	P	E	R	S	A	N	D
F		I			A		C		E		P
O	L	D		B	Y	S	T	A	N	D	E	R
R		E		R		S		D			O
S	O	D	I	U	M		J	E	T	S	A	M
A			S		L		M		W		I
K	E	T	C	H		E	L	I	C	I	T	S
E		O		E		V		C		R		E
N	O	W	A	D	A	Y	S		P	L	O	D

Solution 82

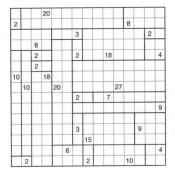

Solution 83

Solution 84

75	76	78	79	80	45	44	40	39	38
74	77	85	84	83	81	46	43	41	37
73	86	88	89	96	82	49	47	42	36
72	87	90	95	97	100	50	48	35	32
68	71	91	94	99	98	51	34	33	31
67	69	70	92	93	52	25	26	30	29
66	65	64	63	53	24	3	1	27	28
60	61	62	54	23	18	2	4	5	6
58	59	55	22	19	17	14	11	9	7
57	56	21	20	16	15	13	12	10	8

SOLUTIONS

BRAIN TRAINING

Solution 85

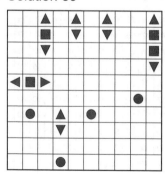

Solution 86

E	V	E	G	A	G	N	E	E	N
R	N	D	D	E	I	O	R	H	O
S	O	A	I	C	V	C	D	P	S
A	C	L	R	E	E	R	L	E	S
T	E	T	P	U	G	N	A	H	F
I	N	O	N	E	N	O	H	P	F
O	E	R	U	O	R	C	A	L	I
N	K	B	M	T	A	P	O	L	R
S	A	E	A	Y	R	E	O	E	A
P	E	R	S	H	E	L	L	R	T

Solution 87

4	3	1	5	8	6	2	7	9
7	6	5	9	2	8	1	4	3
2	9	3	1	4	7	8	6	5
9	8	4	3	1	2	6	5	7
6	7	8	4	5	3	9	1	2
5	1	2	7	6	9	4	3	8
1	5	9	8	3	4	7	2	6
3	2	7	6	9	1	5	8	4
8	4	6	2	7	5	3	9	1

Solution 88

Solution 89

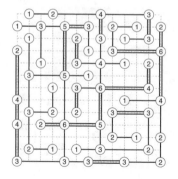

Solution 90

SOLUTIONS

Solution 91

```
C A MAMBA   R   P
R RIA  O T   E   R
ARCR  R T  O PHI
V HOMEOWNER   N
A E O  R A  E  C
TOR  T  ISLES  E
    Y    S  S  S
F  CONTAINERS  S
A  I   O  C   D  E
CONVERGENT  S
T T    R    C
I EAGLE  B OWL
T R   R A I  R O
I PRACTICED  L
OAR V  E E  ILL
U E  E N PEA  O
S T  LASTS  L  P
```

Solution 92

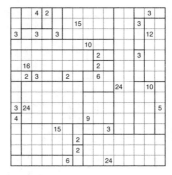

Solution 93

```
APPAL  SNOOZED
S  O  U    B  E
P  S  N  F FJORD
AUTOCRAT  E  I
R  B  H  R ACHED
ACADEMIC  T  A
G  G  D    L M R
U   S  SERENADE
SHOWY  X  G T  D
 A  E APTITUDE
LITRE  I  B R V
 K  V  R  L E  I
QUEENLY  YODEL
```

Solution 94

36	37	38	54	55	70	71	91	93	94
35	39	53	56	69	72	90	92	100	95
34	40	52	57	68	73	89	98	99	96
33	41	51	58	67	74	87	88	97	84
32	42	50	59	63	66	75	86	85	83
31	43	49	60	62	64	65	76	82	81
30	44	47	48	61	19	3	1	77	80
26	29	45	46	20	18	4	2	79	78
25	27	28	21	17	14	12	5	9	8
24	23	22	16	15	13	11	10	6	7

Solution 95

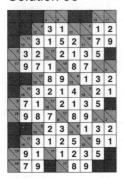

Solution 96

```
A P K E C A O T C A
E P A C E R R L E K
I L E C T O C C D E
N W U R A L O H U D
R O M A S K P P R O
B S B L A A A L T U
E S L E D B L E S G
M N E K I A E M N H
T O B A C E C H U T
E M A E R C A E P S
```

Solution 97

4	7	8	3	2	6	1	9	5
2	6	3	5	1	9	4	7	8
1	9	5	6	8	4	2	3	7
9	1	4	2	7	8	3	5	6
7	3	2	9	5	1	6	8	4
5	8	7	4	6	3	9	1	2
8	5	9	1	4	2	7	6	3
3	2	6	8	9	7	5	4	1
6	4	1	7	3	5	8	2	9

Solution 98

Solution 99

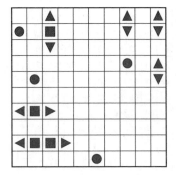

Solution 100

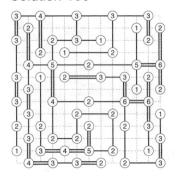

Solution 101

Solution 102

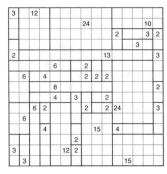

SOLUTIONS

Solution 103

Solution 104

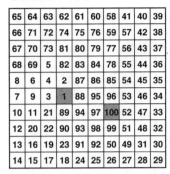

65	64	63	62	61	60	58	41	40	39
66	71	72	74	75	76	59	57	42	38
67	70	73	81	80	79	77	56	43	37
68	69	5	82	83	84	78	55	44	36
8	6	4	2	87	86	85	54	45	35
7	9	3	1	88	95	96	53	46	34
10	11	21	89	94	97	100	52	47	33
12	20	22	90	93	98	99	51	48	32
13	16	19	23	91	92	50	49	31	30
14	15	17	18	24	25	26	27	28	29

Solution 105

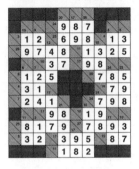

Solution 106

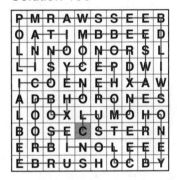

Solution 107

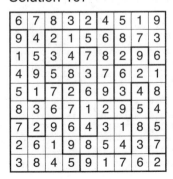

6	7	8	3	2	4	5	1	9
9	4	2	1	5	6	8	7	3
1	5	3	4	7	8	2	9	6
4	9	5	8	3	7	6	2	1
5	1	7	2	6	9	3	4	8
8	3	6	7	1	2	9	5	4
7	2	9	6	4	3	1	8	5
2	6	1	9	8	5	4	3	7
3	8	4	5	9	1	7	6	2

Solution 108

155

SOLUTIONS

Solution 109

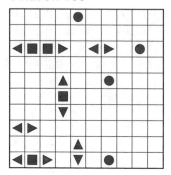

Solution 110

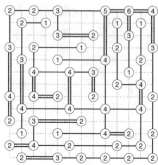

Solution 111

Solution 112

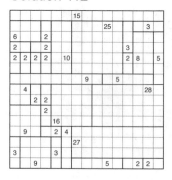

Solution 113

Solution 114

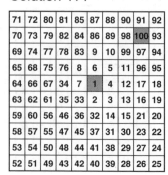

BRAIN TRAINING

SOLUTIONS

Solution 115

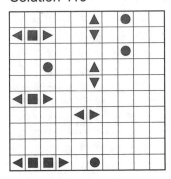

Solution 116

C	A	C	R	O	V	E	E	N
R	L	M	H	C	W	A	O	V	W
E	C	E	E	L	B	Y	R	E	A
L	U	U	Q	L	A	O	T	T	T
U	L	O	R	R	Y	L	T	H	C
R	A	T	S	A	I	D	H	E	R
P	A	T	P	E	E	R	M	O	M
M	G	S	D	E	T	T	E	A	P
A	E	O	O	M	E	E	R	T	E
T	S	P	E	R	U	S	A	E	M

Solution 117

3	1	9	5	2	6	7	8	4
8	6	4	2	7	3	5	9	1
7	8	5	4	9	1	6	3	2
2	4	3	6	8	5	9	1	7
5	7	6	9	1	4	8	2	3
9	3	1	8	5	7	2	4	6
4	2	7	1	6	9	3	5	8
6	5	8	3	4	2	1	7	9
1	9	2	7	3	8	4	6	5

Solution 118

Solution 119

Solution 120

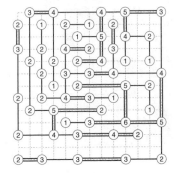

157

SOLUTIONS

Solution 121

```
L S   ION A   K
R O B U S T   O R D A I N
C   P   E   R   O   S
C O O P   M E M O R I S E
M   L     S   A   E
L O C A L E S   A B Y S S
T   N     S   S   L
H I N T   C A N T E E N S
V   U   A   O
R E C O R D E R   C A M E
V   O   E   L   I
O W N E R   I S S U I N G
O   R   B   E   A
A R M C H A I R   L E T S
T   O   L   A   E   I
S H E A R S   F U S I O N
Y   T   A N T   S   N
```

Solution 122

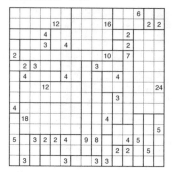

Solution 123

```
A   P   S   S   P   J   Z
X Y L O P H O N E   U S E
L   A   L   R   E   D   N
E X T R A   R A V I O L I
S   F   S   O   E   I   T
  G O S H A W K   M Y T H
H   R   Y   D   O   S
A L M S   A Q U E O U S
L   B   U   C   N   T
C H I M E R A   A U G U R
Y   C   E   R   G   E   A
O N E   F U R I O U S L Y
N   D   Y   Y   N   T   S
```

Solution 124

13	12	10	9	8	88	90	96	97	98
14	15	11	7	87	89	91	95	100	99
17	16	2	4	6	86	92	93	94	82
18	19	3	1	5	76	85	84	83	81
20	21	25	26	57	75	77	79	80	69
22	24	27	56	58	73	74	78	70	68
23	28	53	55	59	62	72	71	67	66
29	51	52	54	60	61	63	64	65	43
30	33	50	49	48	47	46	45	44	42
31	32	34	35	36	37	38	39	40	41

Solution 125

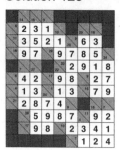

Solution 126

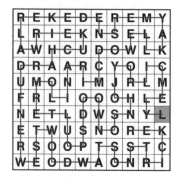

SOLUTIONS

Solution 127

3	9	7	1	8	2	6	5	4
4	6	5	9	3	1	8	2	7
2	5	1	4	7	6	3	8	9
8	1	3	7	2	5	9	4	6
5	7	6	8	4	9	2	1	3
9	4	8	6	1	3	5	7	2
6	2	4	5	9	8	7	3	1
7	3	9	2	5	4	1	6	8
1	8	2	3	6	7	4	9	5

Solution 128

Solution 129

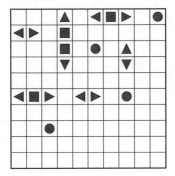

Solution 130

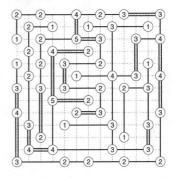

Solution 131

Solution 132

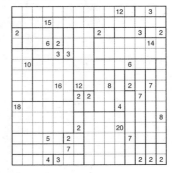

159

SOLUTIONS

Solution 133

BRAIN TRAINING